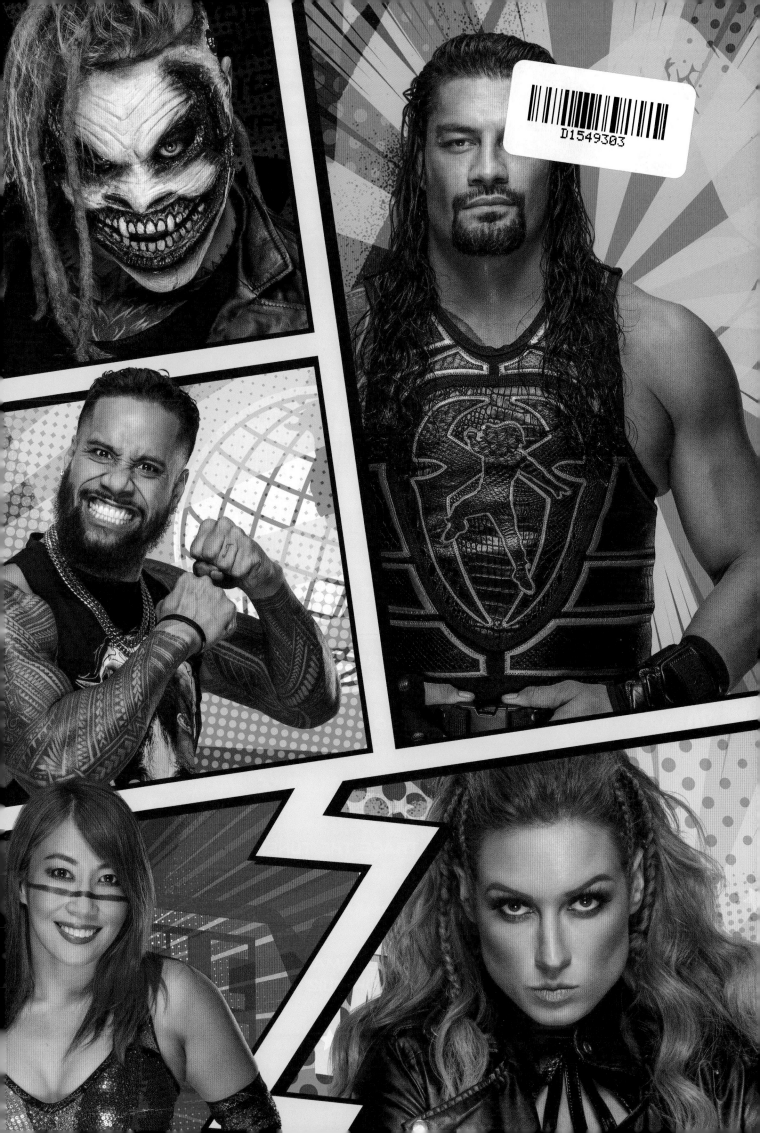

CONTENTS

7 SUPERSTAR WELCOME

8 15 FANTASTIC WRESTLEMANIA FACTS

10 CHAMPIONSHIP MATCH!

12 RAW WOMEN'S TITLE MATCH!

14 THE ULTIMATE RAW QUIZ

16 WHAT'S THE DIFFERENCE?

17 ADD 'EM UP!

18 BONEYARD MATCH!

20 MATCH MIX UP!

21 SUPERSTAR STRETCH

22 THE WORLD'S CHAMPIONS

24 UNIVERSAL CHAMPIONSHIP MATCH!

26 MATCH THE MASKS

27 POINT OUT THE PPVS

28 RING RELATIVES!

30 WHO WORE WHAT?

32 FIREFLY FUNHOUSE MATCH!

34 TRACE THE TUNE!

35 ROMAN-A-GRAMS

36 THE ULTIMATE NXT UK QUIZ

LEGIT

BOSS

38 SMACKDOWN TAG TEAM TITLE TRIPLE THREAT MATCH!

40 DRAW YOUR OWN LOGO

41 PHOTOGRAPHIC MEMORY

43 TEST YOUR TITLE KNOWLEDGE

44 B-I-N-LET'S-GO!

46 WWE AROUND THE WORLD!

48 NXT WOMEN'S CHAMPIONSHIP MATCH!

50 ALL HAIL WWE'S KINGS AND QUEENS

52 WHO IS MR. MONEY IN THE BANK?

53 LAUGH OUT LOUD

54 CONNECT THE TAG TEAMS

56 NO DISQUALIFICATION MATCH!

57 INTERCONTINENTAL TITLE MATCH!

58 WWE WOMEN'S TAG TEAM CHAMPIONSHIP MATCH!

59 THE SHOW OF SHOWS

60 ELIAS VS KING CORBIN

61 OTIS VS DOLPH ZIGGLER

62 THE TOUGHEST NXT QUIZ EVER!

64 SHOW-STOPPING ENTRANCES!

66 LAST MAN STANDING MATCH!

67 HIGH FLYING FUN!

68 CRAZY MAZE

69 CAN YOU SPOT THE CAMOUFLAGE?

70 FATAL FIVE-WAY MATCH!

72 MY NICKNAME IS...

74 THE SUPER SMACKDOWN QUIZ

76 ANSWERS

Published 2020.
Little Brother Books, Ground Floor, 23 Southernhay East, Exeter, Devon, EX1 1QL
Printed In Poland.
books@littlebrotherbooks.co.uk | www.littlebrotherbooks.co.uk
The Little Brother Books trademark, email and website addresses, are the sole and exclusive properties of Little Brother Books Limited.
All WWE programming, talent names, images, likenesses, slogans, wrestling moves, trademarks, logos and copyrights are the exclusive property of WWE and its subsidiaries. All other trademarks, logos and copyrights are the property of their respective owners.

This Book Belongs to

· ·

WELCOME, WWE UNIVERSE

IT'S A NEW YEAR AND THAT MEANS IT'S TIME FOR AN ALL-NEW 2021 WWE ANNUAL! LIKE ME, YOUR WWE CHAMPION DREW MCINTYRE, YOU'RE ALL THE CHOSEN ONES BECAUSE YOU GET TO SEE WHAT SECRETS WE SHARED INSIDE THIS AWESOME BOOK!

EVERY PAGE IS PACKED WITH EXPLOSIVE ACTION, BRAIN-BENDING PUZZLES AND THE COOLEST WWE GAMES YOU CAN'T FIND ANYWHERE ELSE. TEST YOUR SUPERSTAR STRENGTH BY TAKING ALL FOUR ULTIMATE QUIZZES ON YOUR FAVORITE WWE SHOWS: *RAW, SMACKDOWN, NXT* AND *NXT UK*. CAN YOU EARN A PERFECT SCORE?

YOU CAN EVEN JOIN ME AS WE RELIVE *WRESTLEMANIA 36*'S MONUMENTAL MATCHES! LET'S RING THE BELL AND KICK THINGS OFF WITH 15 MIND-BLOWING *WRESTLEMANIA* FACTS YOU CAN WOW YOUR FRIENDS WITH. WELL, WHAT ARE YOU WAITING FOR? TURN THE PAGE!

15 FANTASTIC WRESTLEMANIA FACTS

The Show of Shows is the greatest WWE event of the year and these amazing facts about it are enough to make you shout "WOOOOO!"

Florida has hosted more **WrestleManias** than any other place (**WrestleManias**, 24, 28, 33 and 36!).

In addition to The Streak, Undertaker holds another record: "Most **WrestleMania** Matches" with 27.

More people attended **WrestleMania 32** than any other Show of Shows: 101,763 members of the WWE Universe!

Prior to **WrestleMania 36** (held on Saturday and Sunday), **WrestleMania 2** was the only Show of Shows not held on a Sunday. It aired on a Monday.

More than 1.6 million people have attended The Show of Shows since WWE hosted **WrestleMania 1** in 1985.

The Rock holds the record for the shortest **WrestleMania** win. He pinned Erick Rowan in six seconds at **WrestleMania 32**.

Shawn Michaels won the longest **WrestleMania** match ever, pinning Bret Hart for the WWE Title in 61 minutes, 52 seconds.

At **WrestleMania 35**, Kofi Kingston became the first-ever African-born Superstar to win the WWE Title.

Only two Superstars have won two titles at a single **WrestleMania**: Becky Lynch and Ultimate Warrior.

The first women's main-event match was Charlotte Flair vs. Becky Lynch vs. Ronda Rousey at **WrestleMania 35**.

There have been 153 title matches at **WrestleMania**.

"Macho Man" Randy Savage competed in the most matches at a single **WrestleMania** with four—and he won them all!

WrestleMania 36 marked the first time an NXT title was defended at The Show of Shows.

There has only been 1 Money in the Bank cash-in at The Show of Shows: Seth Rollins at **WrestleMania 31**.

Asuka had a record-breaking 267 win-streak until Charlotte Flair defeated her at **WrestleMania 34**.

WRESTLEMANIA
CHAMPIONSHIP MATCH!

The Chosen One took on The Next Big Thing for the WWE Championship in one of the most explosive matches of the year!

DREW MCINTYRE

DREW MCINTYRE'S JOURNEY TO HIS FIRST WWE CHAMPIONSHIP VICTORY WAS A LONG AND ROCKY ONE--ALMOST 13 YEARS! HE EARNED HIS OPPORTUNITY TO CHALLENGE BROCK LESNAR BY WINNING THE *2020 ROYAL RUMBLE* MATCH.

BROCK LESNAR BEGAN HIS SIX-MONTH REIGN AS WWE CHAMPION BY DEFEATING KOFI KINGSTON FOR THE WIN IN JUST 6 SECONDS ON *SMACKDOWN!* HE PUT HIS TITLE ON THE LINE AT THE SHOW OF SHOWS.

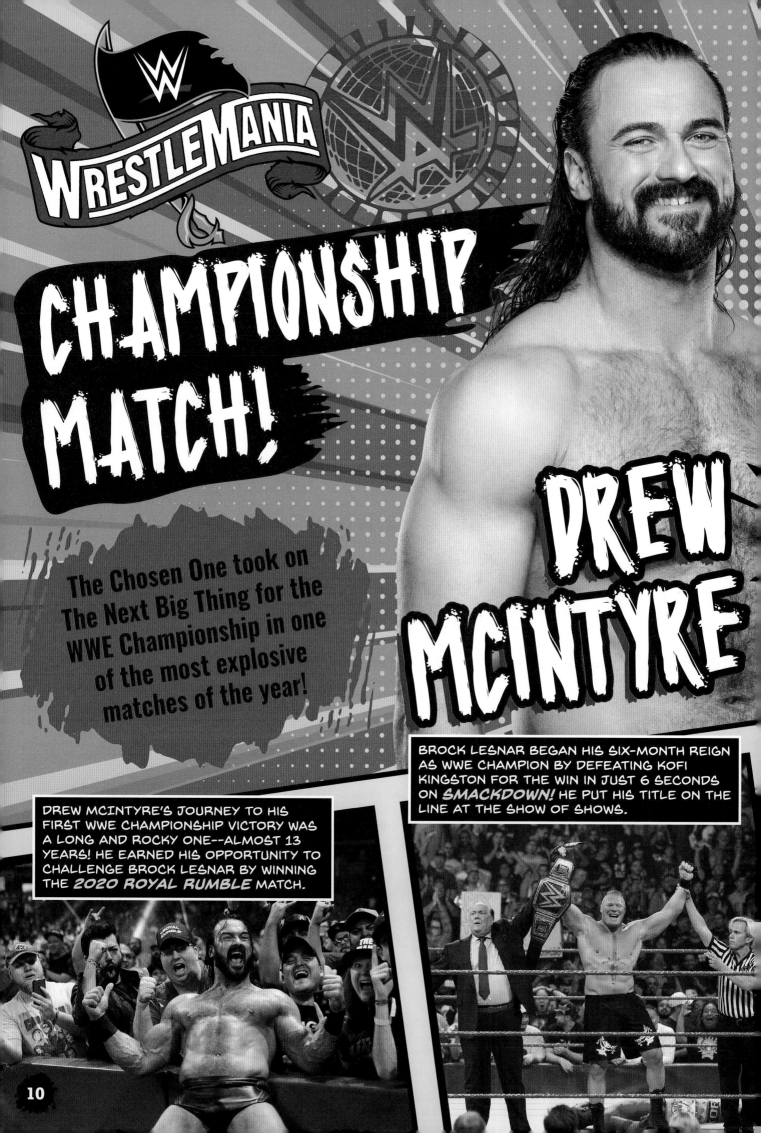

BROCK LESNAR

VS.

THE CHOSEN ONE RETURNED WITH THREE OF HIS OWN SIGNATURE CLAYMORES TO PIN LESNAR AND BECOME THE NEW WWE CHAMPION.

THE BATTLE WAS UPHILL FOR MCINTYRE AS LESNAR HIT THE SCOTTISH SUPERSTAR WITH NOT ONE BUT *THREE* F-5S.

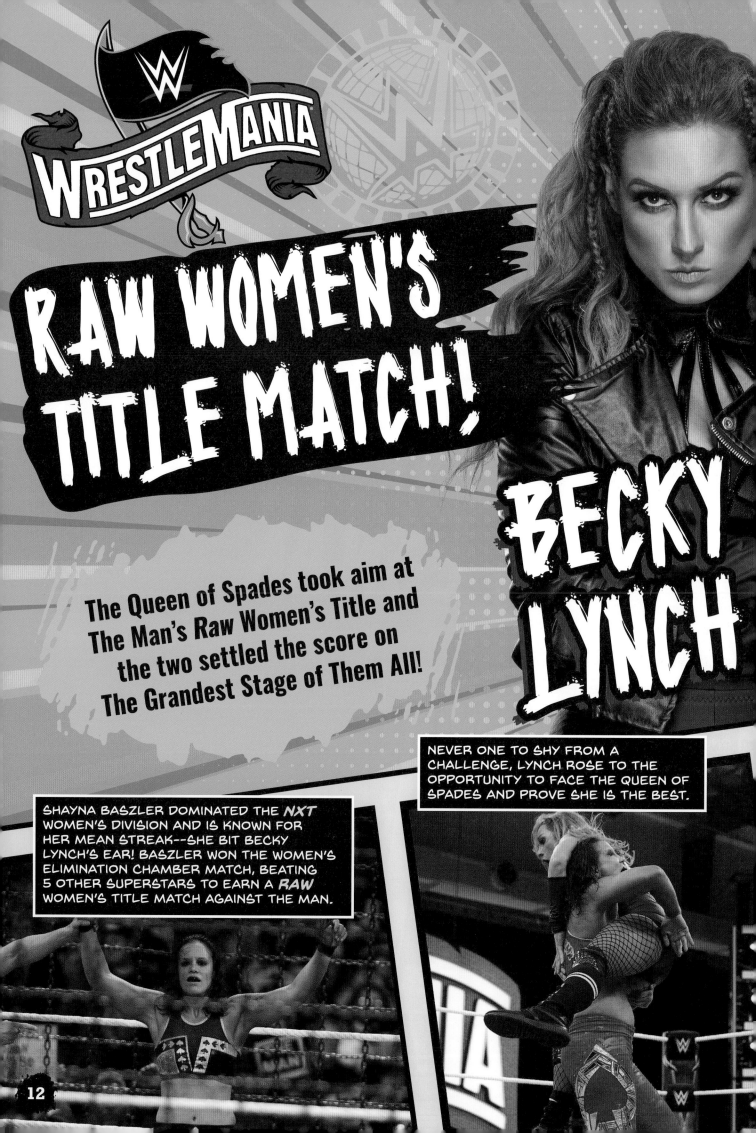

WRESTLEMANIA

RAW WOMEN'S TITLE MATCH!

BECKY LYNCH

The Queen of Spades took aim at The Man's Raw Women's Title and the two settled the score on The Grandest Stage of Them All!

NEVER ONE TO SHY FROM A CHALLENGE, LYNCH ROSE TO THE OPPORTUNITY TO FACE THE QUEEN OF SPADES AND PROVE SHE IS THE BEST.

SHAYNA BASZLER DOMINATED THE *NXT* WOMEN'S DIVISION AND IS KNOWN FOR HER MEAN STREAK--SHE BIT BECKY LYNCH'S EAR! BASZLER WON THE WOMEN'S ELIMINATION CHAMBER MATCH, BEATING 5 OTHER SUPERSTARS TO EARN A *RAW* WOMEN'S TITLE MATCH AGAINST THE MAN.

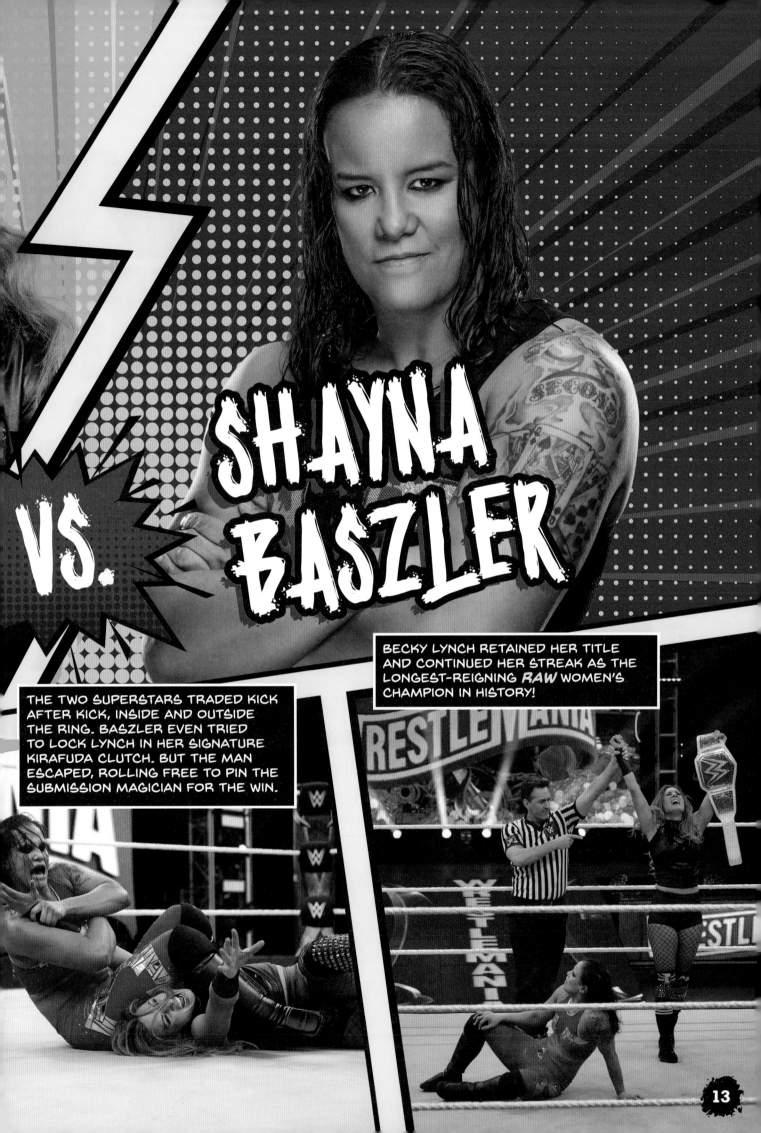

VS. SHAYNA BASZLER

BECKY LYNCH RETAINED HER TITLE AND CONTINUED HER STREAK AS THE LONGEST-REIGNING *RAW* WOMEN'S CHAMPION IN HISTORY!

THE TWO SUPERSTARS TRADED KICK AFTER KICK, INSIDE AND OUTSIDE THE RING. BASZLER EVEN TRIED TO LOCK LYNCH IN HER SIGNATURE KIRAFUDA CLUTCH. BUT THE MAN ESCAPED, ROLLING FREE TO PIN THE SUBMISSION MAGICIAN FOR THE WIN.

THE ULTIMATE WWE RAW QUIZ

How well do you know Monday's longest-running weekly sports entertainment program? Put your minds to the mat and answer these 10 tough teasers about Team Red.

1 Raw first aired on what date?

A. November 18, 1991
B. January 11, 1993
C. May 24, 1994
D. September 10, 1995

2 The first Superstar drafted from *Raw* to SmackDown in 2002 was

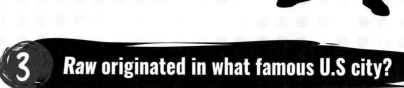

3 Raw originated in what famous U.S city?

A. Boston
B. Los Angeles
C. New York
D. Orlando

4 Charlotte Flair won the first *Raw* Women's Championship battle at which *WrestleMania*?

A. 32
B. 33
C. 34
D. 35

5 True or False: Undertaker competed in the first-ever *Raw* main event.

TRUE ☐ FALSE ☐

6 Which of these countries has not hosted an episode of *Raw*?

A. The United Kingdom
B. Mexico
C. Canada
D. New Zealand

7 John Cena's record 16 title wins is tied with which legendary Superstar?

A. Bret Hart
B. Brock Lesnar
C. Hulk Hogan
D. Ric Flair

8 True or False: In the beginning, *Raw* used to air on Wednesday nights.

TRUE ☐ FALSE ☐

9 Unscramble the letters to name the *NXT* Champion who debuted on *Raw* to answer the John Cena U.S. Open Challenge.

IKNVE ESNWO

10 Which is the only Superstar below to make his debut on *Raw*?

A. Goldberg
B. Rey Mysterio
C. Kane
D. Big Show

Answers on pages 76-77

WHAT'S THE DIFFERENCE

These two action-packed photos are almost perfectly identical! There are 10 tiny differences, though, that only the toughest champs can find. Can you circle them all? In under two minutes? Set the timer and go for it!

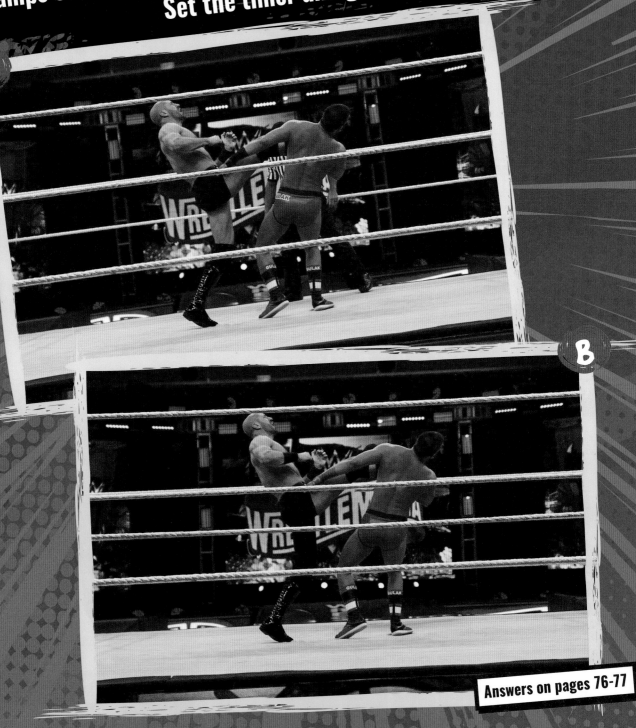

A

B

Answers on pages 76-77

ADD 'EM UP!

Math plays a part in everything we do, from homework to shopping to counting a pinfall: 1, 2, 3, winner! Calculate the missing sum by using the clues below.

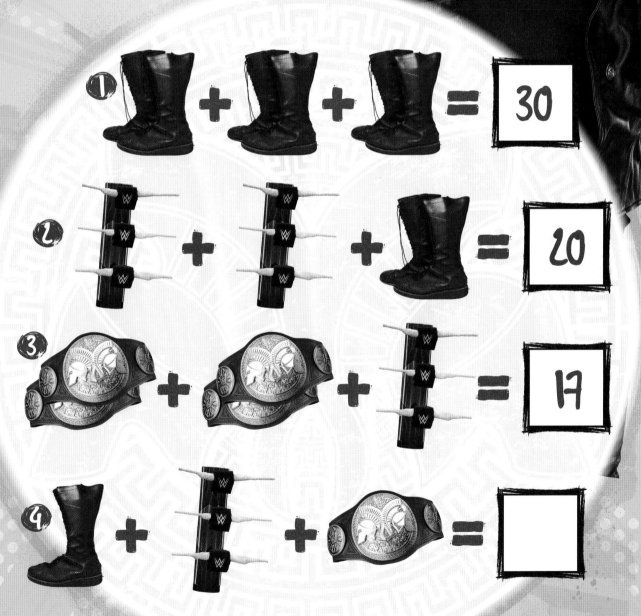

Answers on pages 76-77

WRESTLEMANIA

BONEYARD MATCH!

UNDERTAKER

The Phenomenal One was no match for The Phenom, who buried him in WWE's first-ever Boneyard Match.

AN ANGRY AJ STYLES CALLED UNDERTAKER WASHED UP, AND CHALLENGED HIS FOE TO THE FIRST-EVER BONEYARD MATCH AT *WRESTLEMANIA* 36. THE PHENOMENAL ONE ARRIVED IN A COFFIN, MOCKING HIS OPPONENT. BUT THE DEADMAN RODE IN, READY TO STRIKE.

WHILE AT *WWE SUPER SHOWDOWN*, AJ STYLES WAS ABOUT TO WIN THE TUWAIQ MOUNTAIN TROPHY GAUNTLET MATCH WHEN UNDERTAKER SURPRISED HIM AND SEIZED IT. THE DEADMAN ROSE AGAIN AT *WWE ELIMINATION CHAMBER*, PAVING THE WAY FOR ANOTHER LOSS FOR AJ STYLES, THIS TIME BY ALEISTER BLACK.

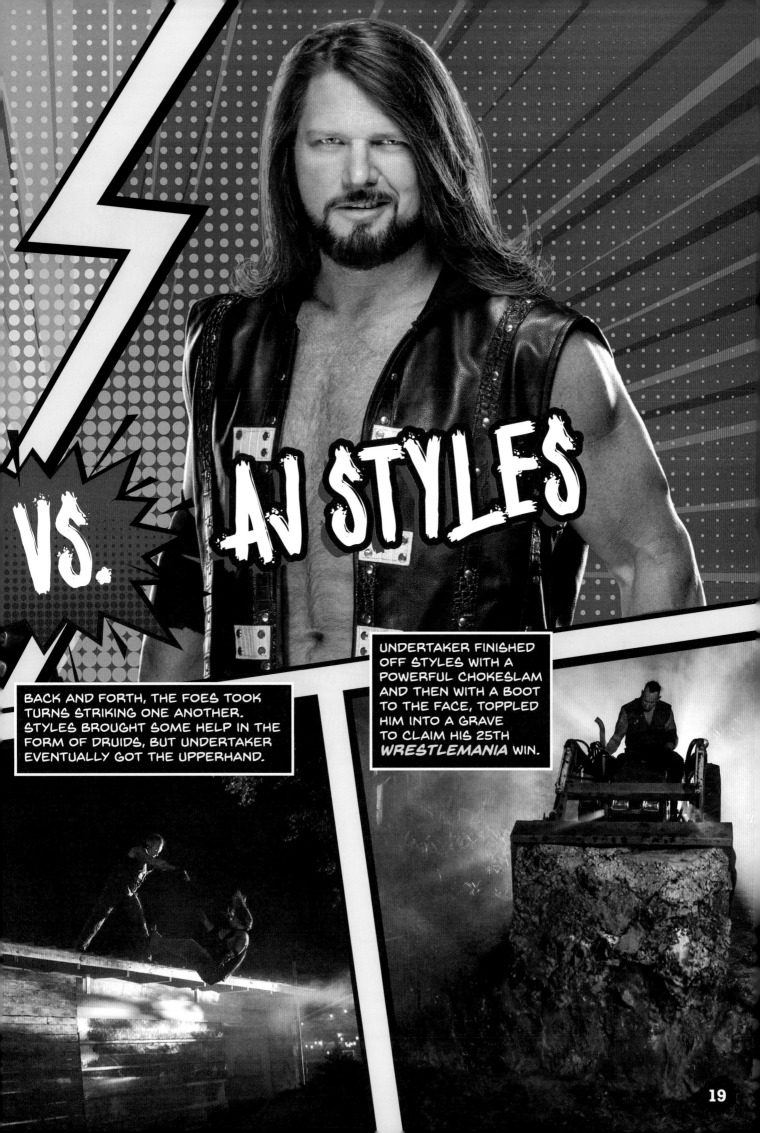

VS. AJ STYLES

BACK AND FORTH, THE FOES TOOK TURNS STRIKING ONE ANOTHER. STYLES BROUGHT SOME HELP IN THE FORM OF DRUIDS, BUT UNDERTAKER EVENTUALLY GOT THE UPPERHAND.

UNDERTAKER FINISHED OFF STYLES WITH A POWERFUL CHOKESLAM AND THEN WITH A BOOT TO THE FACE, TOPPLED HIM INTO A GRAVE TO CLAIM HIS 25TH *WRESTLEMANIA* WIN.

MATCH MiX UP!

While some WrestleMania matches are wins by pinfall or submission, others change up the rules or occur in places like a steel cage or boneyard! Can you unscramble the type of match these Superstars competed in?

1

Edge vs. Randy Orton:

S.ATL ANM NSGTIDNA

2

Brock Lesnar vs. Dean Ambrose:

ERSTET HTIGF

3

Triple H vs. Batista:

ON LOHDS REBDAR

4

Edge vs. John Cena vs. Big Show:

ERTILP HRATTE

5

Shane McMahon vs. The Miz:

LSLAF UTOCN YEEWNHRA

6

Shawn Michaels vs. Bret Hart:

RONI NMA

7

Becky Lynch vs Charlotte Flair vs Ronda Rousey:

NERIWN ETKA LAL

Answers on pages 76-77

20

SUPERSTAR STRETCH

It's almost impossible to read the Superstar name stretched below. Guess the riddle, then tilt the page down to reveal the answer!

RIDDLE: This Superstar won the inaugural 16-man single-elimination tournament to become the first WWE United Kingdom Champion.

Answers on pages 76-77

THE WORLD'S CHAMPIONS

Drew McIntyre made history as WWE's first Scottish WWE Champion. See what other countries some of WWE's favorite world champs call home!

FUN FACTS!

Drew McIntyre started training to be a Superstar when he was 15 years old!

When he debuted, Mr. McMahon called him a "future World Champion." WOW!

The Chosen One earned his World Title opportunity by winning the 30-Man Royal Rumble Match in January 2020, and defeated Brock Lesnar at WrestleMania 36 to capture his first WWE Title!

BRET HART
CANADA

EDGE
CANADA

CHRISTIAN
CANADA

KEVIN OWENS
CANADA

SHEAMUS &
FINN BALOR
IRELAND

PAIGE
ENGLAND

ANDRE THE
GIANT
FRANCE

BRUNO
SAMMARTINO
ITALY

KOFI
KINGSTON
GHANA

JINDER
MAHAL
INDIA

ASUKA
JAPAN

WRESTLEMANIA

UNIVERSAL CHAMPIONSHIP MATCH! GOLDBERG

For years, The Monster Among Men had come so close to winning the Universal Championship, but never quite captured the gold. That all changed during this titanic matchup with Goldberg!

GOLDBERG WAS FEARLESS FROM THE START OF THE MATCH WITH A KICK TO STROWMAN, FOLLOWED BY THREE CONSECUTIVE SPEARS. AND THEN A FOURTH!

BRAUN STROWMAN CAME SO CLOSE TO WINNING THE UNIVERSAL CHAMPIONSHIP, MOST MEMORABLY AGAINST BROCK LESNAR AND SETH ROLLINS. TAKING ON WWE HALL OF FAMER GOLDBERG, WHO WAS A DOMINANT FORCE, SEEMED IMPOSSIBLE.

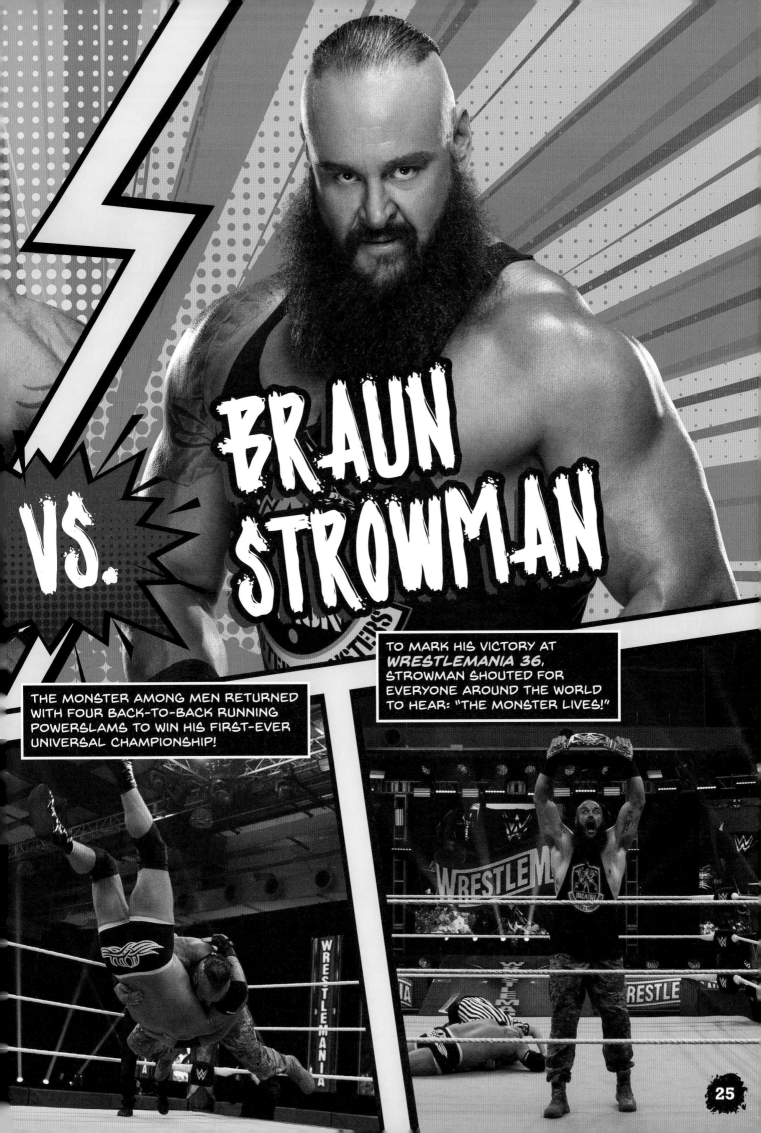

VS. BRAUN STROWMAN

THE MONSTER AMONG MEN RETURNED WITH FOUR BACK-TO-BACK RUNNING POWERSLAMS TO WIN HIS FIRST-EVER UNIVERSAL CHAMPIONSHIP!

TO MARK HIS VICTORY AT *WRESTLEMANIA 36*, STROWMAN SHOUTED FOR EVERYONE AROUND THE WORLD TO HEAR: "THE MONSTER LIVES!"

MATCH THE MASKS

Masks can conceal identities, tell a story, or just plain terrify the WWE Universe. Can you correctly identify the Superstars who are famous for wearing each of these masks?

Rey Mysterio

Kane

Mankind

The Fiend

Kalisto

Gran Metalik

Lince Dorado

Answers on pages 76-77

POINT OUT THE PPVS

It's easy to spot a WWE PPV when it's on TV, but can you find them hidden amongst this jumble of letters? Search across, down and diagonal for all 20 words below!

X	T	G	S	L	S	D	R	E	F	Z	U	H	P	F	X	T	T	G	S
L	T	L	R	E	U	C	F	U	M	V	O	I	H	X	W	A	A	R	U
N	A	M	L	W	M	C	I	Z	L	E	B	A	J	O	B	N	I	H	R
M	W	C	W	E	M	H	S	B	Y	E	R	Y	J	L	Y	A	B	U	V
J	R	O	H	J	E	Z	B	E	O	C	S	T	E	V	H	K	O	N	I
R	X	F	R	A	R	K	N	V	G	T	C	S	X	C	A	Y	E	S	V
W	O	W	A	C	M	O	T	R	P	Z	S	Q	S	E	N	E	U	X	O
O	Q	M	K	D	M	P	R	I	K	E	J	Z	I	E	V	F	C	H	R
N	X	D	A	Y	Y	E	I	H	S	A	L	C	S	R	R	R	T	D	K
O	Z	A	D	Q	H	R	X	O	L	U	W	K	U	L	S	I	C	K	F
R	O	Y	A	L	F	T	O	L	N	N	Z	Q	E	X	R	M	E	Q	A
Z	O	O	W	T	S	E	H	X	A	S	Z	M	Q	J	E	U	B	S	M
G	Y	M	T	I	N	L	Q	C	E	Y	F	R	O	T	D	T	I	B	U
F	P	J	M	M	F	R	A	I	H	S	X	G	A	B	D	B	C	Q	O
A	U	B	B	I	O	V	U	M	C	C	X	K	P	A	A	W	G	E	Y
E	L	I	M	I	N	A	T	I	O	N	E	V	Q	N	L	F	B	V	U
O	D	Q	M	R	U	M	B	L	E	O	J	B	Y	K	Q	Z	N	Y	V
R	E	B	M	A	H	C	F	P	V	T	Q	F	I	M	W	N	U	I	B
F	E	W	K	O	K	V	U	E	Q	Q	Y	E	M	J	B	B	I	P	N
L	Z	G	W	W	V	X	R	R	P	Q	S	R	K	Y	S	F	I	N	D

bank	crown	money	slam
chairs	elimination	royal	summer
chamber	extreme	rules	survivor
champions	jewel	rumble	tables
clash	ladders	series	takeover

Answers on pages 76-77

27

You don't have to be a super smarty pants to know that Nikki and Brie Bella are sisters. But is your brain powerful enough to match the Superstars on the left to their brawlin' relatives on the right?

RING

1 Shane McMahon: My sister is _____.

3 Natalya: My dad is _____.

4 Roman Reigns: My dad is _____.

2 Jimmy & Jey Uso: Our cousin is _____.

6 Randy Orton: My dad is _____.

5 Charlotte Flair: My dad is _____.

RELATIVES!

A
B
C
D
E
F

Answers on pages 76-77

29

WHO WORE WHAT?

While almost anyone can recognize a Superstar by their face, only a true fan can guess the grappler by their gear. Name the Superstars at The Show of Shows.

5

6

7

8

9

10

NAOMI
LACEY EVANS

ASUKA
SHAYNA BASZLER

RHEA RIPLEY
NIKKI CROSS

KOFI KINGSTON
MANDY ROSE

KAIRI SANE
OTIS

Answers on pages 76-77

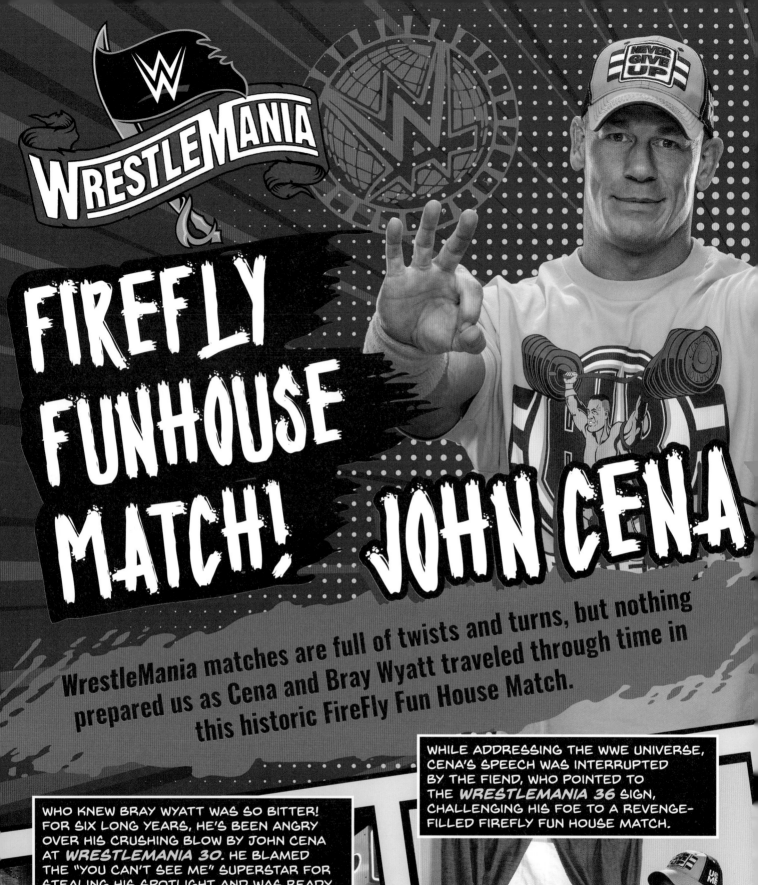

FIREFLY FUNHOUSE MATCH!

JOHN CENA

WrestleMania matches are full of twists and turns, but nothing prepared us as Cena and Bray Wyatt traveled through time in this historic FireFly Fun House Match.

WHO KNEW BRAY WYATT WAS SO BITTER! FOR SIX LONG YEARS, HE'S BEEN ANGRY OVER HIS CRUSHING BLOW BY JOHN CENA AT *WRESTLEMANIA 30*. HE BLAMED THE "YOU CAN'T SEE ME" SUPERSTAR FOR STEALING HIS SPOTLIGHT AND WAS READY FOR PAYBACK.

WHILE ADDRESSING THE WWE UNIVERSE, CENA'S SPEECH WAS INTERRUPTED BY THE FIEND, WHO POINTED TO THE *WRESTLEMANIA 36* SIGN, CHALLENGING HIS FOE TO A REVENGE-FILLED FIREFLY FUN HOUSE MATCH.

ELIMINATION CHAMBER
A WEEK FROM SUNDAY

RESPECT.

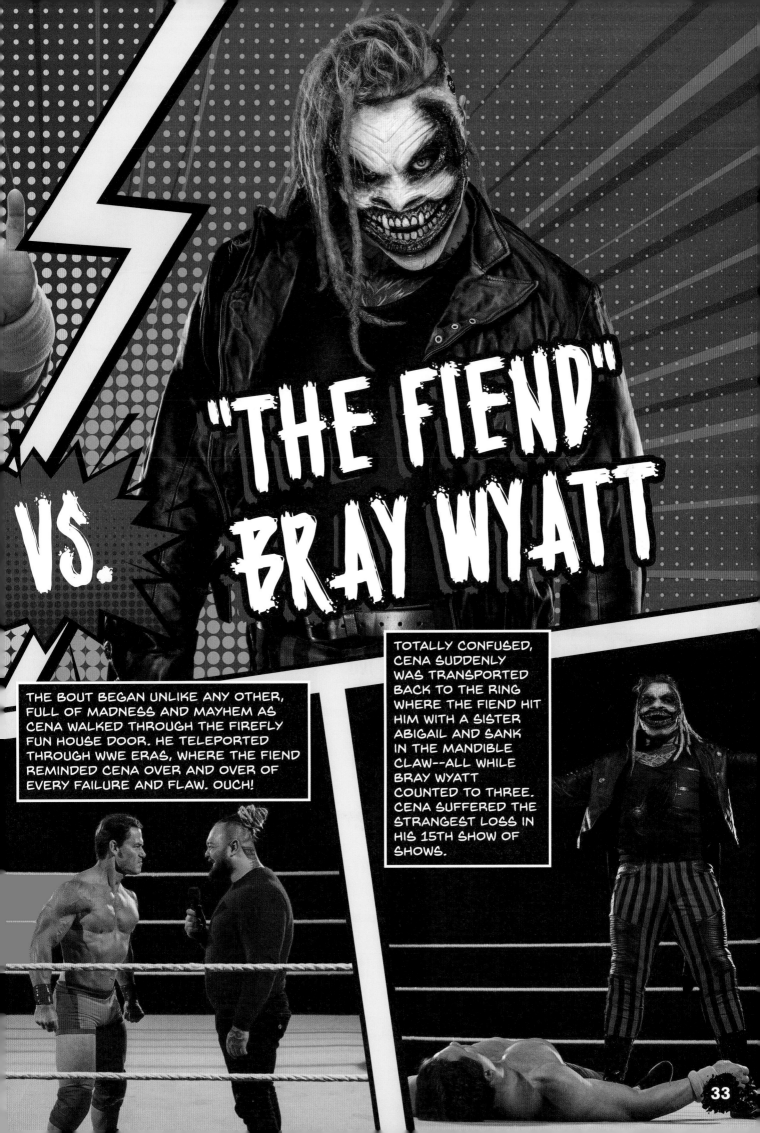

"THE FIEND" BRAY WYATT

VS.

THE BOUT BEGAN UNLIKE ANY OTHER, FULL OF MADNESS AND MAYHEM AS CENA WALKED THROUGH THE FIREFLY FUN HOUSE DOOR. HE TELEPORTED THROUGH WWE ERAS, WHERE THE FIEND REMINDED CENA OVER AND OVER OF EVERY FAILURE AND FLAW. OUCH!

TOTALLY CONFUSED, CENA SUDDENLY WAS TRANSPORTED BACK TO THE RING WHERE THE FIEND HIT HIM WITH A SISTER ABIGAIL AND SANK IN THE MANDIBLE CLAW--ALL WHILE BRAY WYATT COUNTED TO THREE. CENA SUFFERED THE STRANGEST LOSS IN HIS 15TH SHOW OF SHOWS.

33

TRACE THE TUNE!

Sure, you can recognize John Cena's famous entrance song the second it blasts onto your television screen. But do you know the words well enough to sing the theme from start to finish?

FINISH

NOW	IS	TIME	MY	ME
IT'S	THE	FRANCHISE	CAN'T	SEE
NOW	IS	BOY	YOU	NOW
MY	TIME	TIME	I'M	SHINING
ME	CAN'T	IS	MY	UP
SEE	YOU	NOW	IS	TIME

START

YOUR...

Answers on pages 76-77

34

ROMAN-A-GRAMS

The Big Dog is all twisted up! Using the clues below and only the letters in Roman Reigns' name, can you solve the missing words below?

ROMAN REIGNS

1. Jewelry for your ears are _ _ _ r _ _ _ _.

2. "The Queen" is another n_ _ _ for Charlotte Flair.

3. Elias likes to play the guitar and _ i _ _.

4. Becky Lynch is The _ a _.

5. How old you are is your a _ _.

6. Wash your hands to avoid spreading g _ _ _ _.

7. Kofi Kingston loves to play video _ _ _ e _.

8. Jeff Hardy's also known as The Charismatic E_ _ _ _ _.

9. If it's not the afternoon or night, it's _ _ r _ _ _ _.

10. A bell makes this sound "_ i _ _-a-ling-a-ling!"

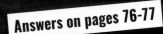
Answers on pages 76-77

THE ULTIMATE QUIZ

Can you crown yourself the know-it-all of all things *NXT UK*? Let's find out!

1

Rearrange these numbers to decipher the date *NXT UK* debuted on WWE Network.

20 10 18 17

2

Toni Storm's nickname is:

A. The Lightning Down Under
B. The Thunder Down Under
C. The Bossy Aussie,
D. The Strongest Storm

3

How many Superstars competed in the tournament to crown the first-ever WWE United Kingdom Champion?

A. 8   C. 16
B. 12   D. 24

4

Unscramble the name of the venue where *NXT UK* takes place.

**DRACFIF
ALANTONI
ARANE**

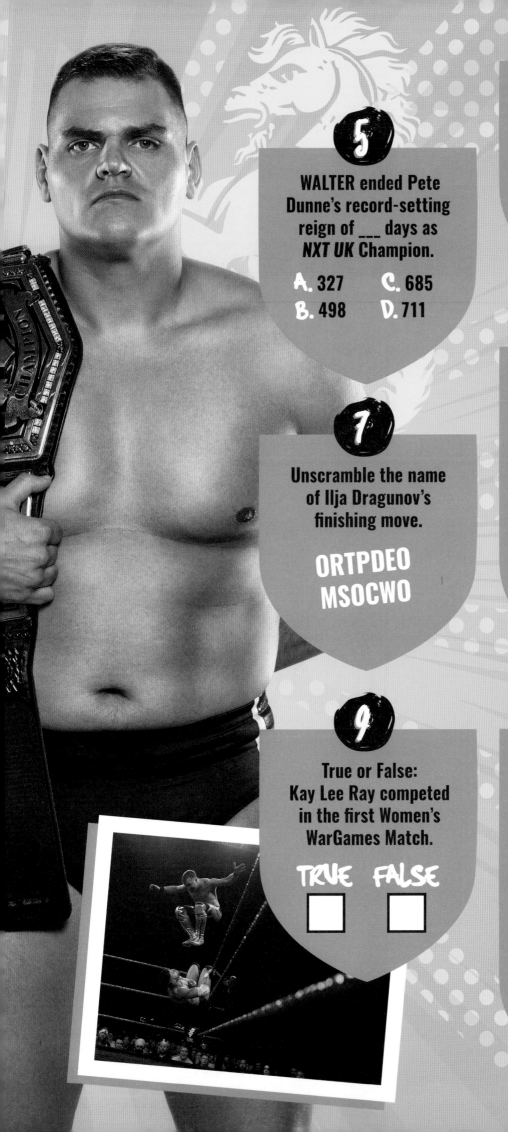

5

WALTER ended Pete Dunne's record-setting reign of ___ days as *NXT UK* Champion.

A. 327   C. 685
B. 498   D. 711

6

Which is NOT an *NXT UK* TakeOver?

A. Glasgow
B. Cardiff
C. Blackpool
D. Dublin

7

Unscramble the name of Ilja Dragunov's finishing move.

ORTPDEO MSOCWO

8

At *NXT UK TakeOver: Blackpool*, The Grizzled Young Veterans performed a "Ticket to Mayhem" on _____ to become the first *NXT UK* Tag Team Champions.

A. Dave Mastiff
B. Trent Seven
C. Joe Coffey
D. Tyler Bate

9

True or False: Kay Lee Ray competed in the first Women's WarGames Match.

TRUE ☐   FALSE ☐

10

At what PPV did Jordan Devlin capture the *NXT* Cruiserweight Championship?

A. *NXT UK TakeOver: Cardiff*
B. *NXT UK TakeOver: Blackpool*
C. *NXT UK TakeOver: WarGames*
D. *WWE Worlds Collide*

Answers on pages 76-77

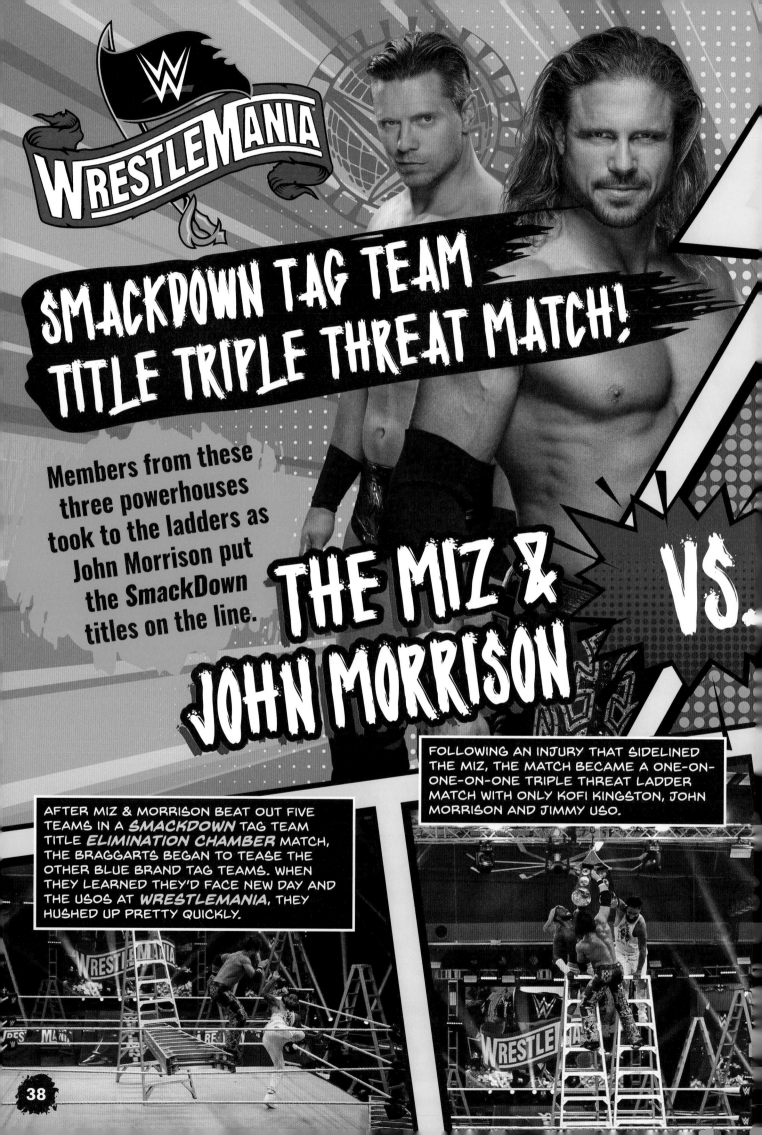

SMACKDOWN TAG TEAM TITLE TRIPLE THREAT MATCH!

Members from these three powerhouses took to the ladders as John Morrison put the SmackDown titles on the line.

THE MIZ & JOHN MORRISON VS.

FOLLOWING AN INJURY THAT SIDELINED THE MIZ, THE MATCH BECAME A ONE-ON-ONE-ON-ONE TRIPLE THREAT LADDER MATCH WITH ONLY KOFI KINGSTON, JOHN MORRISON AND JIMMY USO.

AFTER MIZ & MORRISON BEAT OUT FIVE TEAMS IN A *SMACKDOWN* TAG TEAM TITLE *ELIMINATION CHAMBER* MATCH, THE BRAGGARTS BEGAN TO TEASE THE OTHER BLUE BRAND TAG TEAMS. WHEN THEY LEARNED THEY'D FACE NEW DAY AND THE USOS AT *WRESTLEMANIA*, THEY HUSHED UP PRETTY QUICKLY.

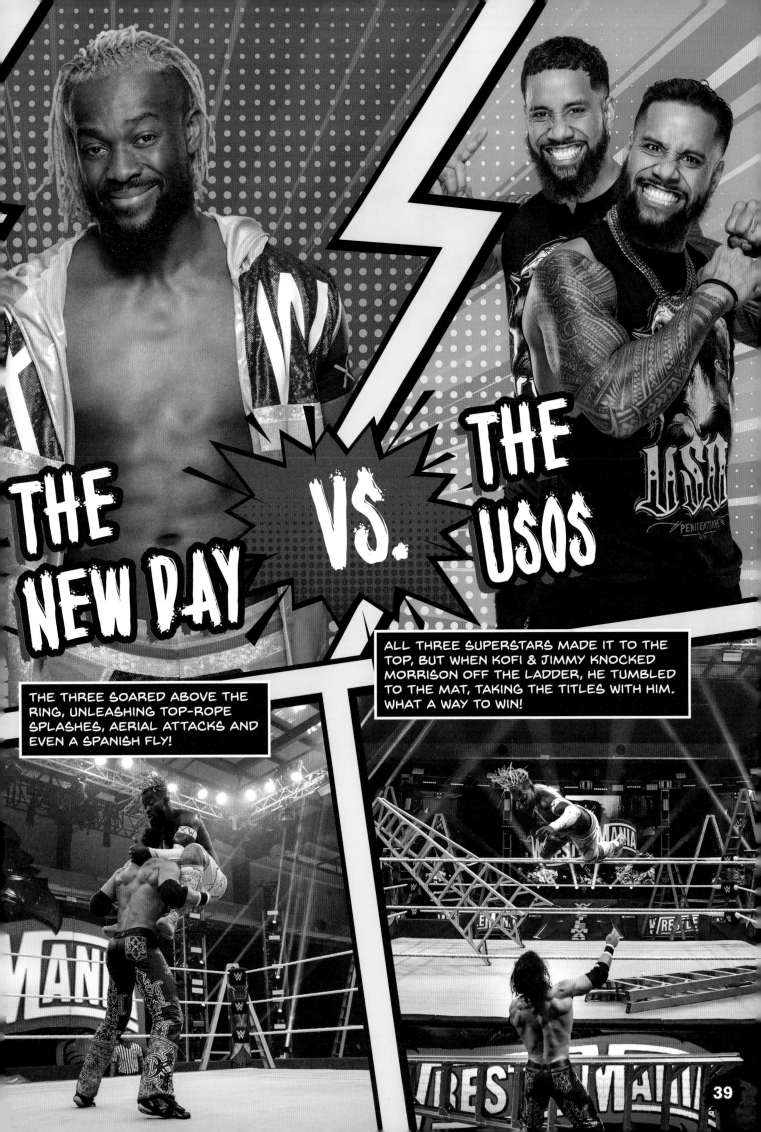

THE NEW DAY

VS.

THE USOS

THE THREE SOARED ABOVE THE RING, UNLEASHING TOP-ROPE SPLASHES, AERIAL ATTACKS AND EVEN A SPANISH FLY!

ALL THREE SUPERSTARS MADE IT TO THE TOP, BUT WHEN KOFI & JIMMY KNOCKED MORRISON OFF THE LADDER, HE TUMBLED TO THE MAT, TAKING THE TITLES WITH HIM. WHAT A WAY TO WIN!

DRAW YOUR OWN LOGO

You don't need a face or a full name to know what Superstars we're talking about here! As the future of WWE, make your mark by designing your own custom WWE logo.

PHOTOGRAPHIC MEMORY

New Day always has the most exciting entrances. Do your best to study every little detail in this photo from *WrestleMania 33*. Set a timer for 60 seconds, then turn the page to answer the questions and see how much you remember!

PHOTOGRAPHIC MEMORY

1. Who is pedaling the ice cream cart?

2. What color are Big E's shoes?

3. How many wheels does the bicycle have?

4. What instrument is Xavier Woods carrying?

5. What animal is on the front of the ice cream cart?

6. Who is the only Superstar wearing sleeves?

7. What color is Kofi's hat?

8. What does Big E's sword say?

9. How many shin guards is Xavier Woods wearing?

10. Is someone wearing a unicorn on their vest?

Answers on pages 76-77

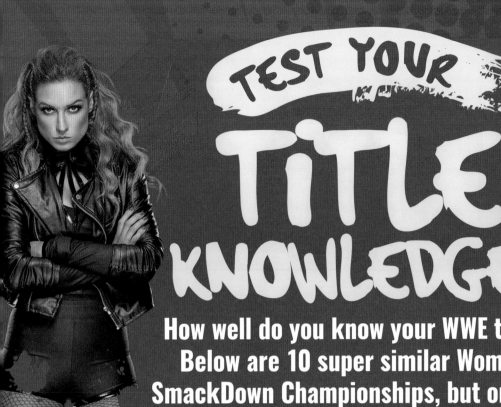

TEST YOUR TITLE KNOWLEDGE!

How well do you know your WWE titles? Below are 10 super similar Women's SmackDown Championships, but only two are identical. Can you figure out which two titles are exactly alike?

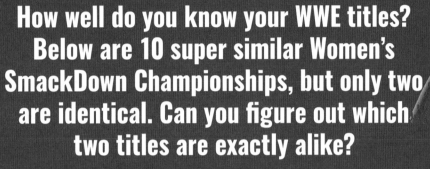

1

2

3

4

5

6

7

8

9

10

Answers on pages 76-77

B-I-N-Let's-GO!

Forget the boring bingo games that only include numbers. Grab a mate to play with and watch SmackDown together, crossing off each image as you spot them on your TV. The first person to complete a line across, down or diagonally wins!

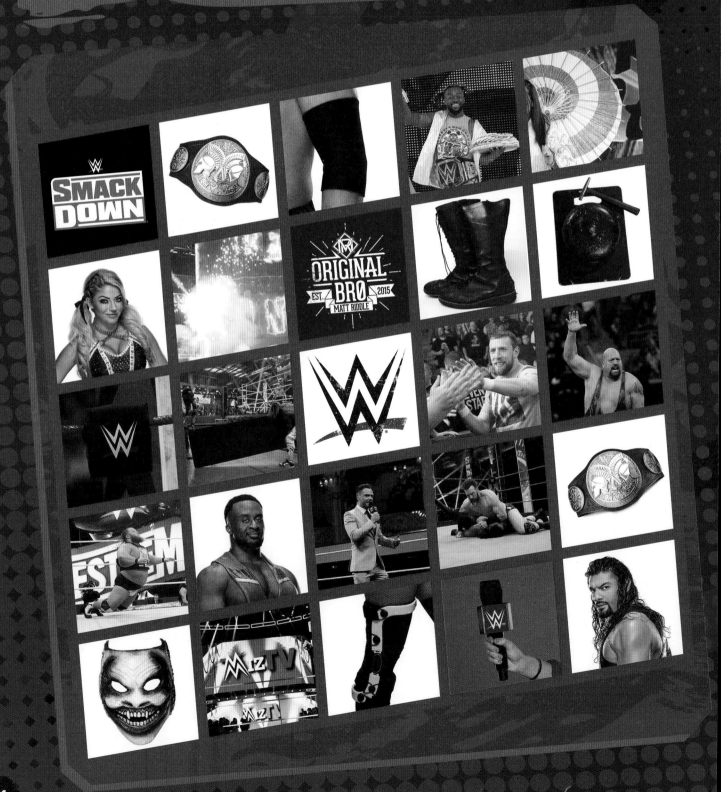

45

WWE AROUND

From India to South Africa, so many Superstars hail from great nations Get out your map and see if you can solve these worldly questions!

1

Yokozuna is a former WWE Champion whose manager, Mr. Fuji, carried this country's flag to the ring.

2

Which Superstar is not from Canada?
A. Natalya
B. Kevin Owens
C. Dolph Ziggler

3

A record-breaking 80,355 members of the WWE Universe attended *SummerSlam 1992* in this European country.

4

Cesaro speaks five languages and his nickname is The _ _ _ _ _ Cyborg.

5

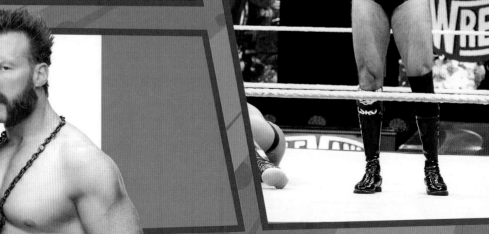

Who was the first Irish-born WWE Champion?

THE WORLD!

6

Both Drew McIntyre and Nikki Cross call this country home.

7

This French Superstar was known as The 8th Wonder of the World.

8

Kofi Kingston made history as the first African-born WWE Champion. In what country was he born?

9

What is the name of the Imperium General who hails from Austria?

10

NXT UK's Toni Storm's home country is also a continent. What is it?

Answers on pages 76-77

NXT WOMEN'S CHAMPIONSHIP MATCH!

RHEA RIPLEY

The Queen has captured almost every women's title in WWE. But when she won an opportunity to take on any opponent at WrestleMania 36, she chose The Nightmare's NXT Title. The next, as they say, is history.

AT *ROYAL RUMBLE*, CHARLOTTE FLAIR OUTLASTED 30 OTHER SUPERSTARS TO WIN A WWE TITLE OPPORTUNITY OF HER CHOICE. HELPING HER MAKE THE DECISION, RHEA RIPLEY TAUNTED HER TO COME HOME TO *NXT* AND TRY TO TAKE THE NXT WOMEN'S TITLE.

THE MATCH BETWEEN CHARLOTTE AND RIPLEY MARKED THE FIRST TIME THAT A SUPERSTAR USED THEIR *ROYAL RUMBLE* WIN TO CHALLENGE FOR AN *NXT* TITLE.

VS. CHARLOTTE FLAIR

RIPLEY WENT DOWN SWINGING, BUT COULDN'T FIGHT FATE. THE QUEEN CAPTURED HER IN A FATEFUL FIGURE-EIGHT THAT FORCED THE NIGHTMARE TO TAP AND RELINQUISH THE BLACK-AND-GOLD'S TOP WOMEN'S TITLE TO MS. WRESTLEMANIA HERSELF.

THE NIGHTMARE TRIED HER BEST TO TAKE OVER THE QUEEN. SHE STRUCK HER OPPONENT WITH HER SIGNATURE RIPTIDE, BUT FLAIR KICKED OUT AT TWO.

ALL HAIL WWE'S KINGS

Superstars aren't really royalty, but they are Kings and Queen in the WWE rings. See if you can crown yourself champion of this noble nickname challenge.

1 The King of Kings is called many things! Which is not a nickname for Hunter Hearst Helmsley?

A. Triple H
B. The Cerebral Assassin
C. The Game
D. The Great One

2 Unscramble the Superstar that Baron Corbin defeated to become 2019's King of the Ring.

HCAD
BLGEA

3 True or False: Jerry "The King" Lawler made his WWE in-ring debut at the 1991 *Royal Rumble*.

TRUE   FALSE

AND QUEENS

4 Charlotte Flair is The Queen for a reason! Circle all the titles she's won.

A B C
D E F

5 Who has not won a King of the Ring tournament?

A. Shawn Michaels
B. Brock Lesnar
C. Stone Cold
D. Sheamus

6 True or False: When Edge won King of the Ring, his nickname was "King Edge the Awesome."

TRUE FALSE ☐

7 Ric Flair's hometown of Charlotte, North Carolina, has this regal nickname:

ENUQE YICT

8 Can you figure out who is this royally named General Manager?

WHO IS

MR. MONEY IN THE BANK?

These 6 Superstars have competed in more Money in the Bank Matches than anyone else in WWE history! Match each Superstar to his total number of entries.

KOFI KINGSTON

SHELTON BENJAMIN

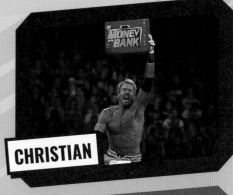

CHRISTIAN

RANDY ORTON

DOLPH ZIGGLER

KANE

RING STATS

BONUS: Who are the only 3 Superstars to have won a Money in the Bank Match?

8   7   6

5   5   5

Answers on pages 76-77

LAUGH OUT LOUD

We have no idea what's going on in this picture, but we can pretend! In the space below, write your silliest caption!

CONNECT THE TAG TEAMS

Montez Ford and Angelo Dawkins together form the tag team with swag: The Street Profits. Can you match these other twosomes to their tag-team name?

1 TEAM HELL NO ☐

2 THE USOS ☐

3 AWESOME TRUTH ☐

4 GRIZZLED YOUNG VETERANS ☐

5 TEAM BAD ☐

Answers on pages 76-77

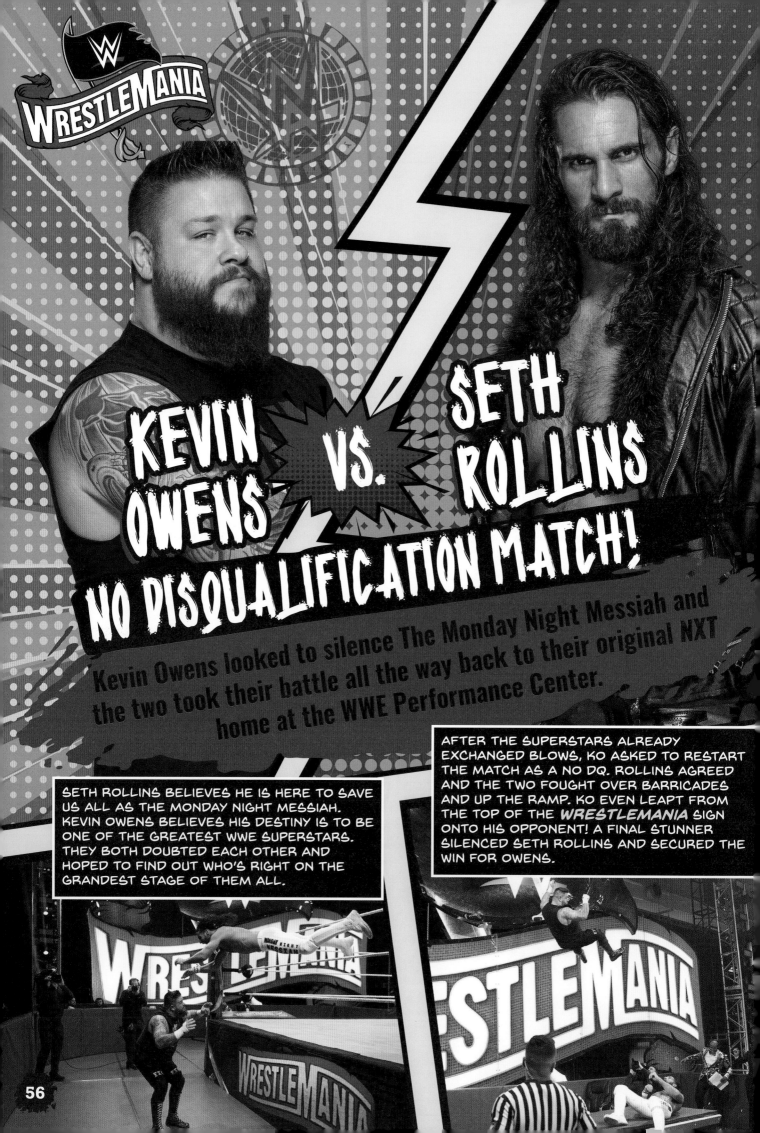

KEVIN OWENS VS. SETH ROLLINS

NO DISQUALIFICATION MATCH!

Kevin Owens looked to silence The Monday Night Messiah and the two took their battle all the way back to their original NXT home at the WWE Performance Center.

AFTER THE SUPERSTARS ALREADY EXCHANGED BLOWS, KO ASKED TO RESTART THE MATCH AS A NO DQ. ROLLINS AGREED AND THE TWO FOUGHT OVER BARRICADES AND UP THE RAMP. KO EVEN LEAPT FROM THE TOP OF THE *WRESTLEMANIA* SIGN ONTO HIS OPPONENT! A FINAL STUNNER SILENCED SETH ROLLINS AND SECURED THE WIN FOR OWENS.

SETH ROLLINS BELIEVES HE IS HERE TO SAVE US ALL AS THE MONDAY NIGHT MESSIAH. KEVIN OWENS BELIEVES HIS DESTINY IS TO BE ONE OF THE GREATEST WWE SUPERSTARS. THEY BOTH DOUBTED EACH OTHER AND HOPED TO FIND OUT WHO'S RIGHT ON THE GRANDEST STAGE OF THEM ALL.

DANIEL BRYAN VS. SAMI ZAYN

INTERCONTINENTAL TITLE MATCH!

WWE's "Yes!" Man aimed to take down Sami Zayn and take home the Intercontinental gold at WrestleMania 36.

NOBODY LIKES BEING LEFT OUT--NOT EVEN SAMI ZAYN! HE DIDN'T TAKE KINDLY TO DANIEL BRYAN TURNING DOWN A CHANCE TO TEAM UP, AND THEN FORMING AN ALLIANCE WITH DREW GULAK. ZAYN, ALONG WITH CESARO AND SHINSUKE NAKAMURA, CAUSED SOME TROUBLE AND THE TWO TOOK THEIR RIVALRY TO THE SHOW OF SHOWS.

THOUGH GULAK HAD DANIEL BRYAN'S BACK AS HE LANDED REPEATED STRIKES ON ZAYN, THE BUDS WERE NO MATCH FOR THE PHILADELPHIA STRETCHER AND HIS COHORTS WHO DISTRACTED BRYAN. WHEN HE TURNED HIS ATTENTION BACK TO THE RING, ZAYN FINISHED HIM WITH A HELLUVA KICK TO RETAIN HIS INTERCONTINENTAL TITLE.

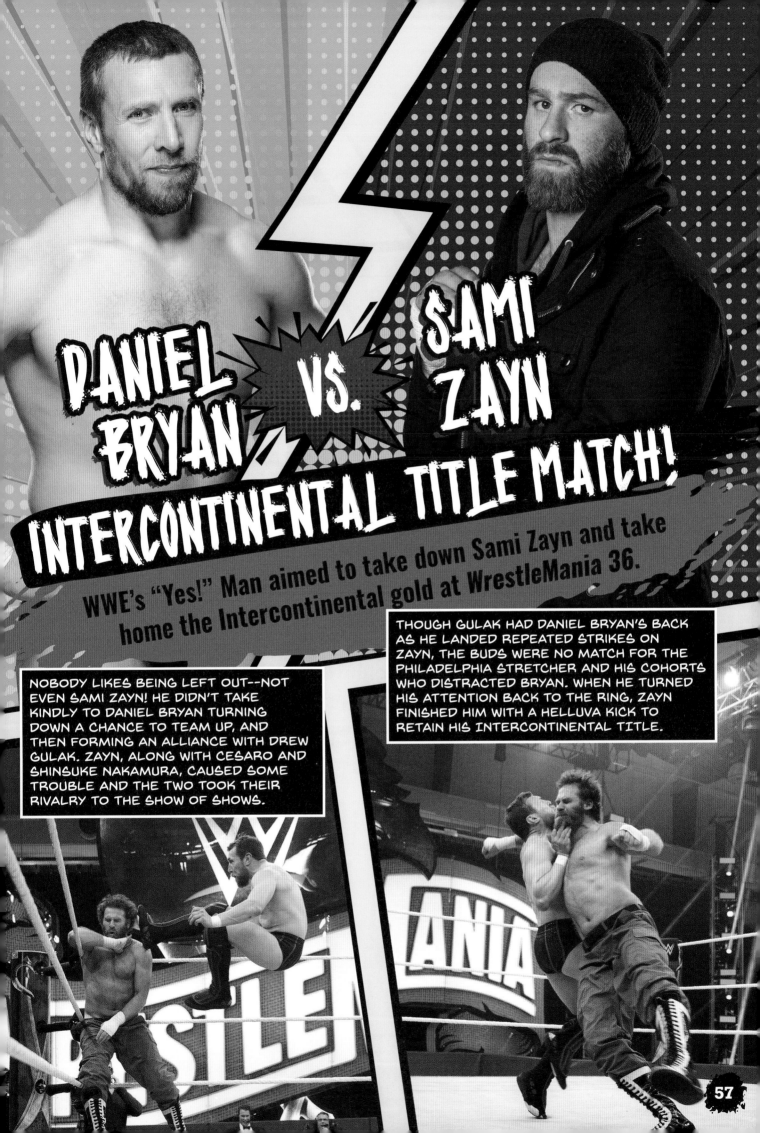

ALEXA BLISS & NIKKI CROSS VS. THE KABUKI WARRIORS

WWE Women's Tag Team Championship Match!

WrestleMania 36 opened with a colorful burst of tag-team power as Bliss & Cross looked to take back the WWE Women's Tag Team Titles.

AT *WWE HELL IN A CELL 2019*, THE KABUKI WARRIORS CAPTURED THE WWE TAG TEAM TITLES FROM ALEXA BLISS & NIKKI CROSS. FOR MONTHS AFTER, ASUKA AND KAIRI SANE'S TRICKS AND MIND GAMES GOT IN THEIR WAY OF THE DUO WINNING THOSE SAME TITLES BACK. THEIR MATCH AT *WRESTLEMANIA 36* AIMED TO PROVE WHO THE GREATEST TAG TEAM OF ALL WAS.

AS THE TWOSOMES GRAPPLED FOR SUPREMACY, IT WAS ALMOST BAD NEWS AS CROSS GOT CAUGHT IN THE ASUKA LOCK--BUT A PERFECTLY TIMED TWISTED BLISS HELPED HER OUT. THE GODDESS OF WWE LATER DELIVERED ANOTHER TO CAPTURE VICTORY, MAKING BLISS & CROSS THE FIRST-EVER TWO-TIME WWE WOMEN'S TAG TEAM CHAMPS.

ALEISTER BLACK VS. BOBBY LASHLEY

Two Superstars look to make a statement as they clash at The Show of Shows.

ALEISTER BLACK WAS TIRED OF WAITING FOR HIS BIG BREAK, THE ONE BIG MATCH TO MAKE HIM THE MOST MEMORABLE SUPERSTAR. BOBBY LASHLEY, ON THE OTHER HAND, WAS LOOKING TO BULLDOZE ANY SUPERSTAR IN SIGHT. COME *WRESTLEMANIA 36*, THE TWO CLASHED WITH LANA AT RINGSIDE.

LASHLEY WAS QUICK TO OVERPOWER HIS OPPONENT, AND WHEN LANA INSISTED HE SPEAR BLACK, HIS DUTCH OPPONENT STRUCK BACK WITH A BLACK MASS--AND EARNED THE BIGGEST WIN OF HIS WWE CAREER TO-DATE.

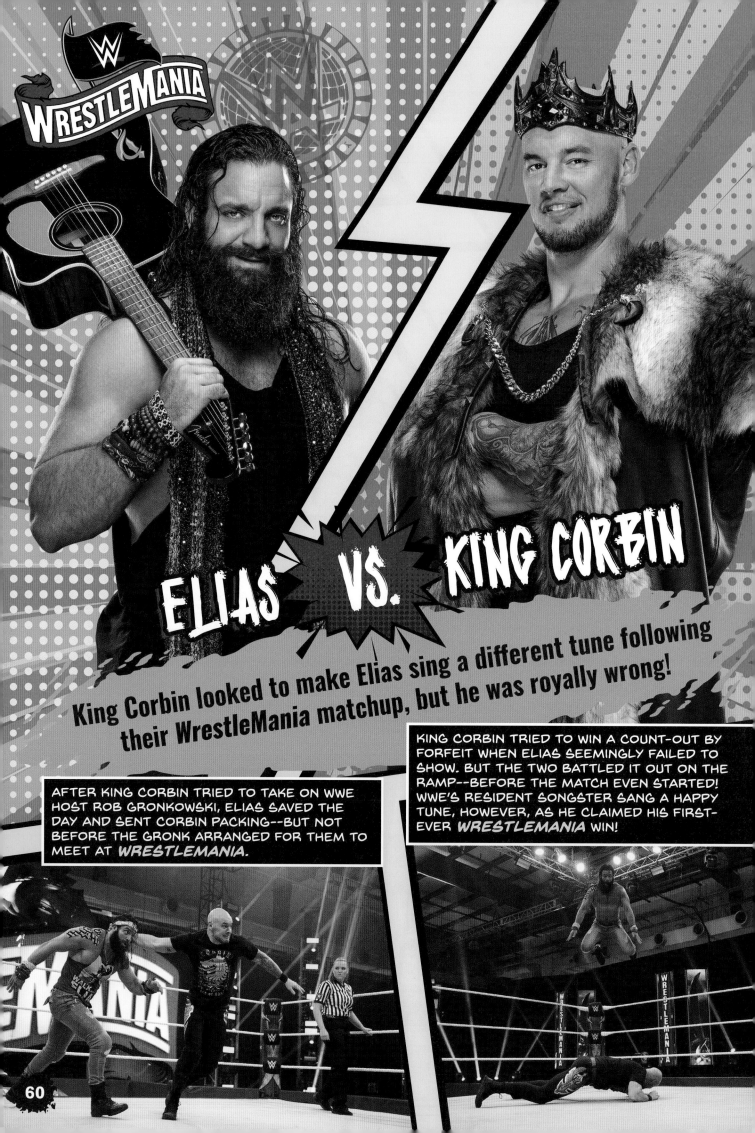

ELIAS VS. KING CORBIN

King Corbin looked to make Elias sing a different tune following their WrestleMania matchup, but he was royally wrong!

AFTER KING CORBIN TRIED TO TAKE ON WWE HOST ROB GRONKOWSKI, ELIAS SAVED THE DAY AND SENT CORBIN PACKING--BUT NOT BEFORE THE GRONK ARRANGED FOR THEM TO MEET AT *WRESTLEMANIA.*

KING CORBIN TRIED TO WIN A COUNT-OUT BY FORFEIT WHEN ELIAS SEEMINGLY FAILED TO SHOW. BUT THE TWO BATTLED IT OUT ON THE RAMP--BEFORE THE MATCH EVEN STARTED! WWE'S RESIDENT SONGSTER SANG A HAPPY TUNE, HOWEVER, AS HE CLAIMED HIS FIRST-EVER *WRESTLEMANIA* WIN!

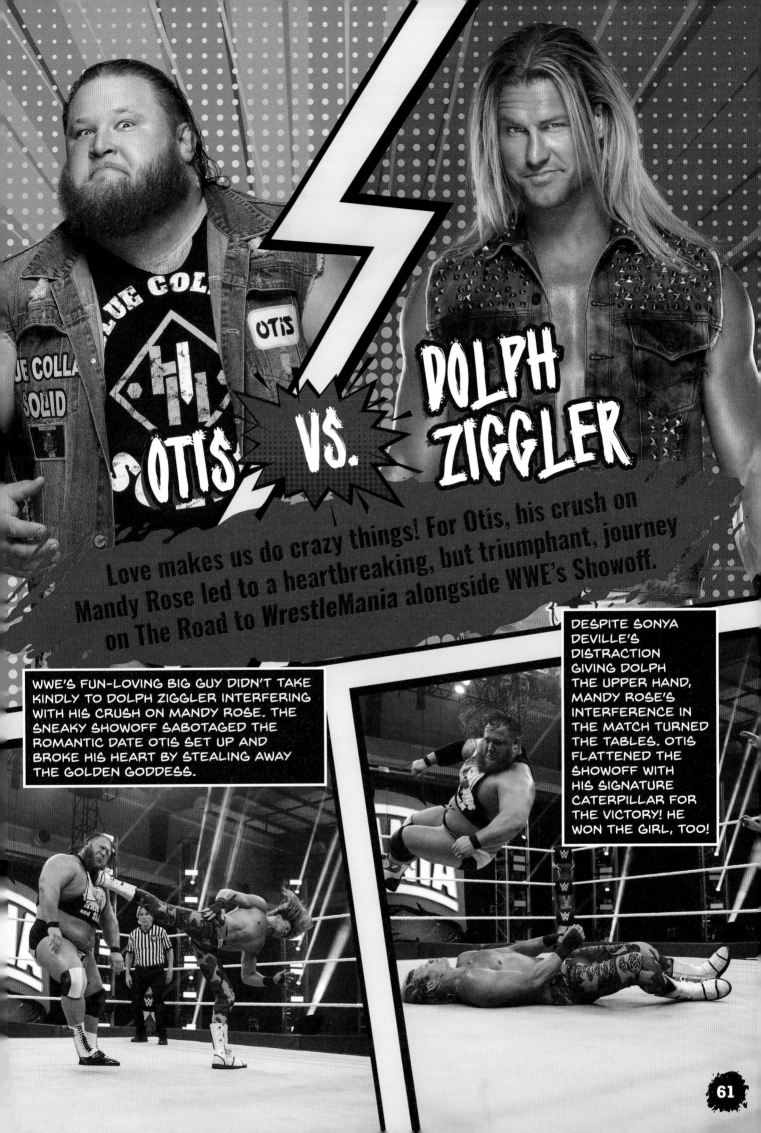

OTIS VS. DOLPH ZIGGLER

Love makes us do crazy things! For Otis, his crush on Mandy Rose led to a heartbreaking, but triumphant, journey on The Road to WrestleMania alongside WWE's Showoff.

WWE'S FUN-LOVING BIG GUY DIDN'T TAKE KINDLY TO DOLPH ZIGGLER INTERFERING WITH HIS CRUSH ON MANDY ROSE. THE SNEAKY SHOWOFF SABOTAGED THE ROMANTIC DATE OTIS SET UP AND BROKE HIS HEART BY STEALING AWAY THE GOLDEN GODDESS.

DESPITE SONYA DEVILLE'S DISTRACTION GIVING DOLPH THE UPPER HAND, MANDY ROSE'S INTERFERENCE IN THE MATCH TURNED THE TABLES. OTIS FLATTENED THE SHOWOFF WITH HIS SIGNATURE CATERPILLAR FOR THE VICTORY! HE WON THE GIRL, TOO!

THE TOUGHEST NXT QUIZ [EVER!]

Test your brain on all things black-and-gold with this explosive quiz!

1 Two of these Superstars have won the NXT Title, NXT North American Title and the NXT Tag Team Title.

A. Adam Cole
B. Johnny Gargano
C. Tommaso Ciampa
D. Keith Lee

2 Order these Dusty Rhodes Tag Team Classic winners from the first in 2015 to 2020.

A. Aleister Black
B. Finn Balor
C. Matt Riddle
D. Kyle O'Reilly

3 Which Superstar is represented by this logo?

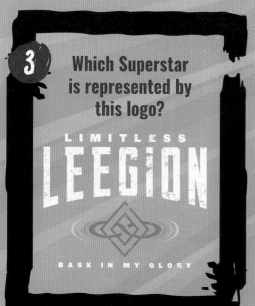

LIMITLESS
LEEGION
BASK IN MY GLORY

4 True or False: Shayna "2-Time" Baszler is the only two-time NXT Women's Champion.

TRUE ☐ FALSE ☐

5 In what U.S. state is Full Sail University located?

A. California
B. Texas
C. New York
D. Florida

6 Unscramble Dominik Dijakovic's finisher:

STEFA
UORY
SYEE

7 Who was NOT a part of Team Rhea's WarGames team in 2019?

A. Candice LeRae
B. Tegan Nox
C. Io Shirai
D. Dakota Kai

8 True or False: Alexa Bliss and Braun Strowman came up from NXT.

TRUE   FALSE

9 At what TakeOver PPV did Adam Cole win the NXT Title?

A. Brooklyn III
B. XXV
C. New York
D. New Orleans

10 What does Mia Yim's HBIC nickname stand for?

_ _ _ _   _ _ _ _ _ _

_ _   _ _ _ _ _ _

Answers on pages 76-77

SHOW-STOPPING

Knock, knock! Who's there? It's your favorite Superstars and their most famous WrestleMania entrances! Using the WrestleMania logos on the opposite page, can you correctly recall the Superstar to The Show of Shows these photos are from?

1

John Cena's .... entrance

2

New Day's .... entrance

ENTRANCES!

3

HHH's . . . . entrance

4

Edge's . . . . entrance

Answers on pages 76-77

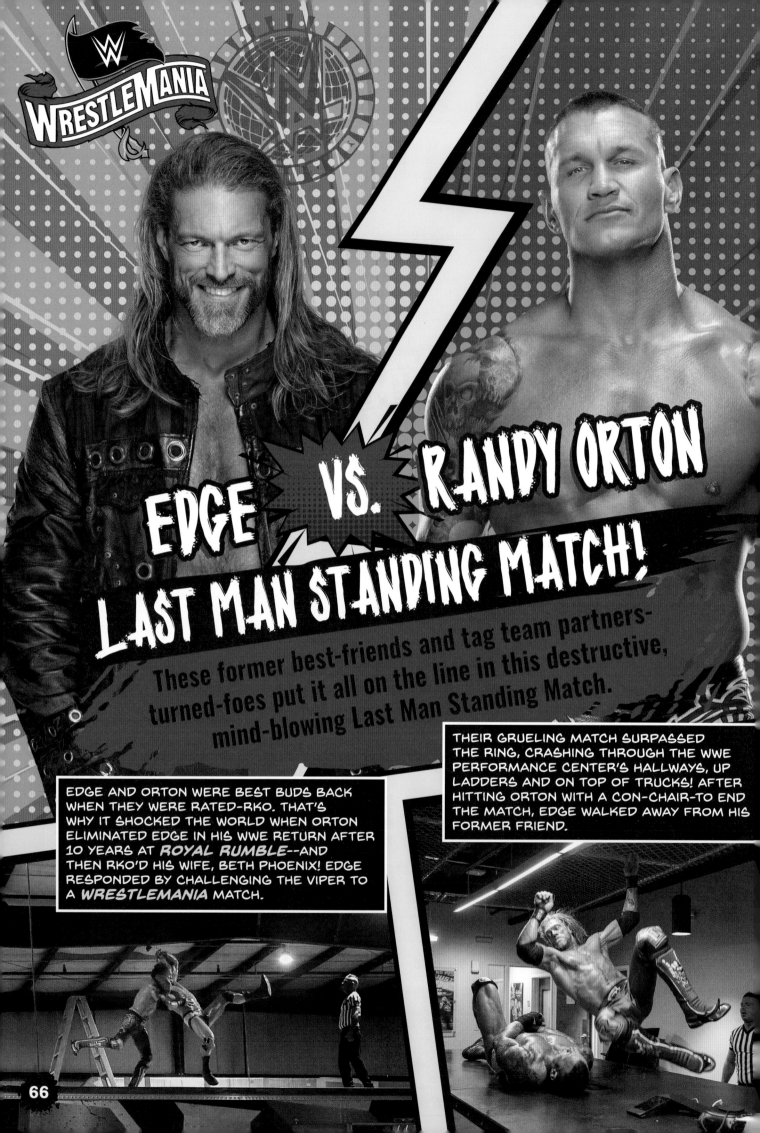

EDGE VS. RANDY ORTON
LAST MAN STANDING MATCH!

These former best-friends and tag team partners-turned-foes put it all on the line in this destructive, mind-blowing Last Man Standing Match.

EDGE AND ORTON WERE BEST BUDS BACK WHEN THEY WERE RATED-RKO. THAT'S WHY IT SHOCKED THE WORLD WHEN ORTON ELIMINATED EDGE IN HIS WWE RETURN AFTER 10 YEARS AT *ROYAL RUMBLE*--AND THEN RKO'D HIS WIFE, BETH PHOENIX! EDGE RESPONDED BY CHALLENGING THE VIPER TO A *WRESTLEMANIA* MATCH.

THEIR GRUELING MATCH SURPASSED THE RING, CRASHING THROUGH THE WWE PERFORMANCE CENTER'S HALLWAYS, UP LADDERS AND ON TOP OF TRUCKS! AFTER HITTING ORTON WITH A CON-CHAIR-TO END THE MATCH, EDGE WALKED AWAY FROM HIS FORMER FRIEND.

HiGH FLYING FUN!

It's a bird! It's a plane! It's a... Superstar! If he wasn't in the ring, where do you think he'd be flying? Over a volcano? Alongside pterodactyls? Is he parachuting over sharks? You decide!

CRAZY MAZE

Uh-oh! WALTER has been separated from his Imperium teammates. Can you help The Ring General find his way to the finish line so that he can reunite with Marcel Barthel, Fabian Aichner and Alexander Wolfe?

START

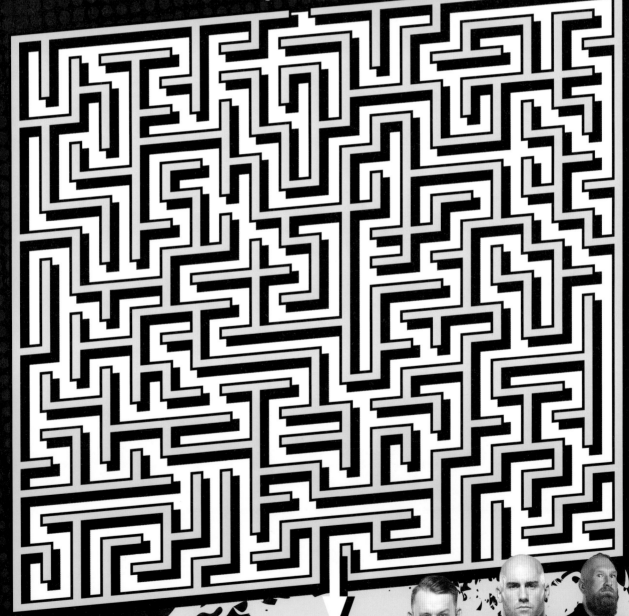

FINISH

Answers on pages 76-77

CAN YOU SPOT THE CAMOUFLAGE?

Camouflage is meant to help a person blend into the background. Can we trick you into thinking there's nothing to see here? Put on your pretend spy glasses and uncover all the hidden WWE gear below.

CAN YOU FIND:

Tommaso Ciampa's trousers

Sgt. Slaughter's gear

Big Show's singlet

Dolph Ziggler's WrestleMania 36 gear

John Cena's shorts

Braun Strowman's trousers

Answers on pages 76-77

FATAL FIVE-WAY MATCH!

BAYLEY VS. SASHA BANKS VS.

Can Bayley retain her title against four of WWE's strongest female Superstars? It might take a little help from Sasha Banks to make it happen.

THIS DIDN'T SIT WELL WITH PAIGE, ONE OF THE PIONEERS OF THE WOMEN'S EVOLUTION. SO SHE SET THEM STRAIGHT BY PUTTING BAYLEY'S TITLE ON THE LINE AGAINST FOUR OTHER SUPERSTARS AT THE SHOW OF SHOWS.

BAYLEY AND SASHA BANKS LOVE TO BRAG! THEY PROCLAIMED THAT NO SUPERSTAR COMPARED TO THE SELF-PROCLAIMED ROLE MODELS AND THAT THEIR ERA OF DOMINANCE HAD BEGUN.

LACEY EVANS VS. TAMINA VS. NAOMI

BANKS SEEMED SUPER ANGRY, BUT SHE RETURNED TO HELP BAYLEY PIN LACEY EVANS FOR THE WIN--AND RECLAIM HER TITLE. TALK ABOUT TRUE FRIENDS!

THOUGH IT WAS EVERY SUPERSTAR FOR HERSELF, THE LOYAL SASHA BANKS SAVED BAYLEY FROM NAOMI'S FTG, HELPING HER TO ELIMINATE THE GLOW. BUT MOMENTS LATER, AN ACCIDENTAL HUG FROM BAYLEY LED TO THE BOSS'S ELIMINATION.

MY NICKNAME is...

It's a badge of honor to earn a nickname, especially one as awesome as "The Great One" or "The Deadman." How well do you know the nicknames of these WWE Superstars? Select the words from the bank and fill out each Superstar's name tag.

1

HELLO
my name is

2

HELLO
my name is

3

HELLO
my name is

4

HELLO
my name is

5

HELLO
my name is

6

HELLO
my name is

7

HELLO
my name is

8

HELLO
my name is

9

HELLO
my name is

10

RING GENERAL

HBIC

BOSTON BRUISER

TWISTED SISTER

PHENOMENAL ONE

SASSY SOUTHERN BELL

PIRATE PRINCESS

THE EST OF NXT

THE BIG DOG

CAPTAIN OF TEAM KICK

Answers on pages 76-77

THE SUPER SMACK DOWN

If you're a member of Team Blue, you should have no trouble acing this pop quiz on all things *SmackDown*!

1

True or False: The word *SmackDown* was added to the Merriam-Webster dictionary in 2007.

TRUE ☐ FALSE ☐

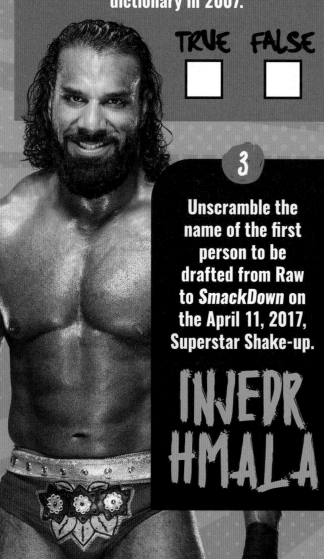

3

Unscramble the name of the first person to be drafted from Raw to *SmackDown* on the April 11, 2017, Superstar Shake-up.

INJEDR HMALA

2

At which event did Becky Lynch defeat five other Superstars to become the first-ever *SmackDown* Women's Champion?

A. WrestleMania   C. SummerSlam
B. Royal Rumble   D. Backlash

4

During a Halloween-themed episode of *SmackDown*, John Cena rapped for the WWE Universe and earned this nickname:

A. Mr. Thuganomics   C. Dr. of Economics
B. Dr. of Thuganomics   D. Vanilla Ice

5

Who captained Team *SmackDown* in 2019's three-way Survivor Series Elimination Match?

AHSSA KBSNA

QUIZ

6

Though she performed Twin Magic, which Bella Twin was credited as debuting first on *SmackDown*: Nikki or Brie Bella?

_____

7

This Superstar holds the record for the longest *SmackDown* reign as World Champion.

A. Brock Lesnar
B. John Cena
C. AJ Styles
D. Kofi Kingston

8

Following her retirement, ___ was given the role as *SmackDown* General Manager.

A. Beth Phoenix
B. Nikki Bella
C. Becky Lynch
D. Paige

9

SmackDown has aired live from 7 different countries! Which one has not hosted the blue brand?

A. Germany
B. Mexico
C. Japan
D. Italy

10

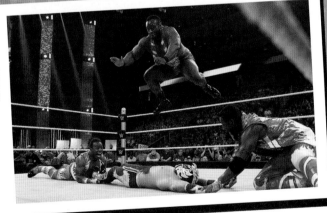

The New Day combine for the most reigns as *SmackDown* Tag Team Champions with how many overall?

A. 4   B. 6   C. 7   D. 9

Answers on pages 76-77

ANSWERS

34
TRACE THE TUNE

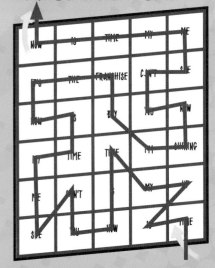

14-15
THE ULTIMATE RAW QUIZ
1. B, 2. The Rock, 3. C, 4. A,
5. True, 6. D, 7. D, 8. False,
9. Kevin Owens, 10. A.

26
MATCH THE MASKS
A. Gran Metalik, B. Kalisto, C. Mankind,
D. Rey Mysterio, E. Lince Dorado, F. Kane,
G. The Fiend

16
WHAT'S THE DIFFERENCE?

27
POINT OUT THE PPVS

35
ROMAN-A-GRAMS
1. earrings, 2. name, 3. sing, 4. Man,
5. age, 6. germs, 7. games, 8. Enigma,
9. morning, 10. ring

17
ADD 'EM UP
Answer: 18

28-29
RING RELATIVES!
1. D, 2. C, 3. F, 4. E, 5. A, 6. B

36-37
THE ULTIMATE NXT UK QUIZ
1. 17/10/2018, 2. A, 3. C, 4. Cardiff
National Arena, 5. C, 6. A, 7. Torpedo
Moscow, 8. B, 9. True, 10. D

20
MATCH MIX UP!
1. Last Man Standing, 2. Street Fight,
3. No Holds Barred, 4. Triple Threat,
5. Falls County Anywhere, 6. Iron Man,
7. Winner Take All

30-31
WHO WORE WHAT?
1. Asuka, 2. Kairi Sane, 3. Kofi Kingston,
4. Lacey Evans, 5. Mandy Rose, 6. Naomi,
7. Nikki Cross, 8. Otis, 9. Rhea Ripley,
10. Shayna Baszler

41-42
PHOTOGRAPHIC MEMORY
1. Kofi, 2. Gold, 3. 3, 4. Trombone,
5. Duck, 6. Big E, 7. Red,
8. New Day, 9. 1, 10. No.

21
SUPERSTAR STRETCH
Tyler Bate

43

TEST YOUR TITLE KNOWLEDGE
3. and 7. are the same

46-47

WWE AROUND THE WORLD!
1. Japan, 2. C, 3. England, 4. Swiss, 5. Sheamus, 6. Scotland, 7. Andre the Giant, 8. Ghana, 9. WALTER, 10. Australia

50-51

ALL HAIL WWE'S KINGS AND QUEENS
1. D, 2. Chad Gable, 3. False: 1993, 4. C, D, E, F, 5. A, 6. True, 7. Queen City, 8. William Regal

52

WHO IS MR. MONEY IN THE BANK
Kane: 8, Kofi Kingston: 7, Christian: 6, Dolph Ziggler, Randy Orton, Shelton Benjamin: 5. Bonus: Dolph Ziggler, Randy Orton & Kane.

54-55

CONNECT THE TAG TEAMS
1. D & F, 2. B & C, 3. A & G, 4. E & H, 5. I & J & K

62-63

THE TOUGHEST NXT QUIZ EVER!
1. A & B, 2. B, D, A, C, 3. Keith Lee, 4. False, 5. D, 6. Feast Your Eyes, 7. C, 8. True, 9. B, 10. Head Baddie in Charge

64-65

SHOW-STOPPING ENTRANCE
1. Wrestlemania 25, 2. Wrestlemania 32, 3. Wrestlemania 30, 4. Wrestlemania 24,

68

CRAZY MAZE

69

CAN YOU SPOT THE CAMOUFLAGE

72-73

MY NICKNAME IS...
1. Boston Bruiser, 2. Twisted Sister, 3. Pirate Princess, 4. Captain of Team Kick, 5. Phenomenal One, 6. Sassy Southern Bell, 7. Ring General, 8. HBIC, 9. The Big Dog, 10. The EST of NXT

74-75

THE SUPER SMACKDOWN QUIZ
1. True, 2. D, 3. Jinder Mahal, 4. B, 5. Sasha Banks, 6. Brie Bella, 7. C, 8. D, 9. A, 10. B